ASCD | arias

MAKING SENSE OF MATH

How to Help Every Student Become a Mathematical Thinker and Problem Solver

Cathy L. **SEELEY**

ASCD

Alexandria, VA USA

NCSM
LEADERSHIP IN MATHEMATICS EDUCATION
NETWORK
COMMUNICATE
SUPPORT
MOTIVATE

Aurora, CO USA

NCTM® | NATIONAL COUNCIL OF TEACHERS OF MATHEMATICS

Reston, VA USA

www.ascd.org
books@ascd.org

www.mathedleadership.org
office@mathedleadership.org

www.nctm.org
publications@nctm.org

Published simultaneously by ASCD, 1703 N. Beauregard Street, Alexandria, VA 22311, the National Council of Supervisors of Mathematics, 2851 S. Parker Road #1210, Aurora, CO 80014, and the National Council of Teachers of Mathematics, 1906 Association Drive, Reston, VA 20191.

Printed in the United States of America. ASCD publications present a variety of viewpoints. The views expressed or implied in this book should not be interpreted as official positions of the Association.

PAPERBACK ISBN: 978-1-4166-2242-0   ASCD product #SF116067

Also available as an e-book (see Books in Print for the ISBNs).

Library of Congress Cataloging-in-Publication Data

Names: Seeley, Cathy L.
Title: Making sense of math : how to help every student become a mathematical thinker and problem solver / Cathy L. Seeley.
Description: Alexandria, Virginia, USA : ASCD, 2016. | Includes bibliographical references and index.
Identifiers: LCCN 2016004887 | ISBN 9781416622420 (pbk. : alk. paper)
Subjects: LCSH: Mathematics--Study and teaching (Elementary)--Handbooks, manuals, etc. | Mathematics teachers--Training of--Handbooks, manuals, etc.
Classification: LCC QA135.6 .S447 2016 | DDC 372.7--dc23 LC record available at http://lccn.loc.gov/2016004887

24 23 22 21 20 19 18 17 16   1 2 3 4 5 6 7 8 9 10

ASCD | arias

MAKING SENSE OF MATH

How to Help Every Student Become a Mathematical Thinker and Problem Solver

Want to earn a free ASCD Arias e-book?
Your opinion counts! Please take 2–3 minutes to give
us your feedback on this publication. All survey
respondents will be entered into a drawing to
win an ASCD Arias e-book.

Please visit
www.ascd.org/ariasfeedback

Thank you!

Introduction

When I learned how to teach mathematics many years ago, it seemed like a fairly straightforward task—prepare well and explain clearly. Whenever I could, I tried to elaborate why a particular procedure worked or a particular kind of problem might be solved a certain way. If I wanted the students to really stay with me, I learned to focus on asking good questions and challenging students to go beyond their comfort zone, always with enthusiasm and a smile on my face. I worked hard to find interesting puzzles and games that might have some slim connection to what I was teaching. And I made myself available for students before and after school. I like to think that I got better every year, and I also like to think that most of my students thought I was a pretty good teacher overall. Many of them came to not hate math, and perhaps they even learned most of what they needed to know in order to move on. I tried not to focus on the fact that the math I was teaching might not have been very relevant to their lives or might not make sense to some students, even with my "clear" explanations.

I've learned a lot since those early days in my teaching career. Today we know much more about what it takes to equip students to become mathematical thinkers who can take on any problem they encounter. We also know that students—all students—have more ability and even more intelligence than we might have imagined. As we think about how to nurture and help students develop their abilities and intelligence, I'm convinced that their success in the future depends at least as much on *how they think* as it does on *what they know*. Likewise, I'm convinced that if we're going to help them succeed, we need to pay at least as much attention to *how we teach* as to *what we teach*. We need to challenge some of our old ideas about struggling and frustration and consider structuring our classrooms differently from how classrooms might have been structured when we were students. We may even need to turn those structures upside down. And we need to recognize that professional learning communities—if used appropriately—can offer a powerful vehicle for teachers to learn how to more effectively help students gain the mathematical knowledge, problem-solving skills, and habits of mind they need for living and working in the 21st century.

In this brief look at mathematics teaching, let's think together about what it takes for every teacher to help every student become a mathematical thinker. To look at broader issues related to prioritizing math at the school level and creating and supporting strong math programs, see my companion volume for leaders, *Building a Math-Positive Culture* (Seeley, 2016).

Who's Smart in Math?

Students have difficulties in mathematics for many reasons. They may have learning problems. They may not speak English as their primary language. They may be too shy to ask questions or have behavior or attendance problems. They may have missed or misunderstood an important concept in the past. They may not see the relevance of what they're learning. But the biggest barrier for many students is their belief that some people are naturally good at math and some people simply aren't. Students come to believe this myth largely because the adults around them, including their parents and teachers, may also believe it. Unfortunately, this idea has been reinforced by some long-standing practices and underlying beliefs, particularly structuring classrooms around teacher-centered lectures, using timed tests to assess mathematical fluency, and believing that good students shouldn't make mistakes.

Traditionally, we may have thought of a "good" or "smart" math student as one who is quick to respond to a teacher's question, accurate at computing the answer to a computation problem, and able to apply a newly learned procedure to solve a word problem. But the truth is that there are many ways to be smart in math. Some students may be creative problem solvers. Others may be visual thinkers who can see and analyze quantitative or spatial relationships.

Still others may be thoughtful, slow processors of information and generators of multifaceted solutions to complex problems. When we expand our ideas about what it means to be smart in math, and when we help students develop their mathematical talents in a variety of ways, we're likely to see many more smart students. Of greater importance, *more students will see themselves as smart.* And when they see themselves that way, they're far more likely to be willing to tackle the next mathematical idea or challenging problem they encounter.

We now know that nearly any student can learn mathematics and succeed if we shift our practice a bit. We'll take a look at some of those shifts shortly. For now, let's consider what it means to be smart—smart in general, and specifically, smart in mathematics.

Mindsets About Intelligence

Thanks to advances in cognitive psychology and technological breakthroughs in studying neural connections in the brain, we now know more about the nature of intelligence than ever before. In the groundbreaking book *Mindset*, Carol Dweck (2006) brought these notions to a broad audience as she discussed the differences between a *fixed mindset* about intelligence and a *growth mindset*. In the past, many people—including some experts—believed that intelligence was all about the genes a person is born with. This fixed notion of intelligence would mean that a person is as smart now as he or she ever was and is ever going to be—that even if someone learns new things, his or her basic intelligence would remain the same.

However, researchers are accumulating a growing body of evidence in support of a growth mindset—the notion that intelligence is far more malleable than some may have thought. We now know that genes are only a starting point in determining a person's intelligence. Researchers studying intelligence and analyzing brain scans of individuals working on different types of problems have found that as people work through an activity that is difficult, they can actually grow new neural connections—in essence, their intelligence increases, and they become smarter. The experiences in a person's life and, more significantly, how that person processes those experiences, can influence that person's intelligence. If someone understands that certain kinds of experiences can increase intelligence, it can influence not only how the person approaches school (especially hard subjects), but even how that person relates to others and functions in everyday life.

Impact of a Student's Mindset

A student's mindset about his or her intelligence plays a huge role in the student's willingness to tackle and persevere through a challenging problem. Imagine how a student with a fixed mindset—who believes he's only as smart as he's ever going to be—reacts when encountering a hard problem that he doesn't know how to solve. He's very likely to believe that the problem is beyond his intelligence and capability. His response may be something like, "You never taught me that. I don't know how to do this. I can't do it."

Ironically, a fixed mindset about intelligence can affect students who see themselves as smart just as negatively as it affects students who see themselves as less smart. The student with a fixed mindset who believe she's smart views any kind of failure as evidence that she's reached her limit of "smartness"—that her innate intelligence has hit its peak. Consequently, she tries at all costs to look smart by providing the right answer and strives to avoid situations in which she might fail, such as tackling a challenging problem.

If, however, a student—either one who sees herself as "smart" or one who doesn't—has come to understand that a person can get smarter by working hard through challenging problems, that student might instead respond by thinking, "Wow. This is a hard problem. I may have to work pretty hard to solve this. It may take me a while." With a growth mindset, both successful and less successful students can become motivated to tackle something they think may be beyond their previous level of success.

Students aren't likely to develop a growth mindset on their own. But we can help them get there. We can teach students about the nature of intelligence, including the findings of recent brain research about a growth mindset. We can help them see the subtle and blatant stereotype threats prevalent in society—for example, "girls can't do math"; "minority students aren't as smart as white students"; "poor children can't learn as well as affluent children"—that may undermine their confidence and the development of their intelligence. The choices a teacher makes about what tasks to assign, how to orchestrate classroom discussion, and how to evaluate and reward learning can have a tremendous influence on a student's mindset about intelligence and on how students view their abilities and potential in mathematics.

Impact of a Teacher's Mindset

A teacher's mindset about intelligence may be at least as important for a student's success as the student's mindset. As much as we may talk about the importance of high expectations for all students, it is all too easy to fall prey to our own unconsciously low expectations for some students. During my Peace Corps experience in Burkina Faso a few years ago, my unconsciously low expectations for students almost kept me from allowing a class to tackle a challenging topic. I was on the verge of deciding to skip the unit on quadratic functions with a class of students who were in the non-math track in my school. A Burkinabè colleague convinced me—actually insisted—that I needed to include it. When I reluctantly did so, I realized how important the experience of working through this challenging content was for my students. When we finished that unit, the class celebrated. They knew they had done something hard. I believed that it would be too hard for them, that they wouldn't get it, that they wouldn't like it, and that they didn't need it. I now know that, in the process of working through something difficult, they may have even grown some new neural connections and become smarter. Even if none of them ever use what they learned outside of that classroom, the experience of working through hard mathematics was rewarding for them, and it was important for their learning, intelligence, and attitudes about mathematics and themselves as math students. It's humbling to this day to realize that I almost withheld that opportunity from them not because of their limitations but because of my own unconscious habits and beliefs. A teacher's underlying beliefs and mindset about intelligence can prevent us from allowing a student or group of students to fully develop their potential. Changing our mindset enables students to engage in and struggle through problems that help them grow smarter.

Mathematics offers a unique proving ground for students to work through challenging problems. As teachers and curriculum developers, we have tremendous power to offer students the kinds of tasks that can help them develop their intelligence.

Implications for Teaching

If we're going to help students see themselves as smart, we need to reconsider the efficacy of some of our long-standing practices. In particular, we should reexamine how often, if ever, teachers should present mathematical procedures via lecture, expecting students to listen and remember what we have presented. Too many students tune out such lectures, seeing them as abstract and unrelated to their lives. Moreover, such a teaching approach reinforces the idea that math is a set of rules and that, in order to succeed, you have to remember which rule to use in which situation. Watching a teacher deliver a step-by-step procedure can make a student believe that the teacher is one of those people for whom mathematics comes easily. If the student doesn't see himself as one of "those" people, the student may disconnect from what the teacher is saying, hoping desperately that he will be able to remember to use that rule at the right time. The double whammy here is that, by teaching in a teacher-centered, listen-and-learn way, we confirm students' wrong ideas about both mathematics and themselves as mathematics students. Watching teachers work through a problem or computation without being engaged with the content themselves can make students believe that math is like magic—and not anything that can make sense. It can reinforce their belief that "I'm probably just not a math person." If a student has adopted a fixed mindset about intelligence, these beliefs can become even more firmly entrenched than otherwise.

The alternative to a *teacher-centered* classroom is a *teacher-structured* classroom focused on student engagement and discussion around rich problems and mathematical ideas. We'll take a look at how such a classroom might operate in the section on "upside-down teaching." For now, consider the possibility that there may be ways to structure classrooms that draw out the best of students' thinking and help them become smarter in the process.

Seeing Below the Surface

There are many ways students may inadvertently hide what they already know, what talents they may have, or how smart they might be or become. If students can't speak English well, it's difficult to know what they know or how they think. If students don't pay attention well or if they act out in class, or even if their work looks sloppy or messy, it's easy to think they aren't smart or motivated to learn. And the various acronyms we may assign students—SPED, ED, ADHD, ELL, and so on—all bring with them the weight of low expectations for students.

With respect to language differences, we need to look for ways to help students express their ideas, even if English is not their primary language. The worst thing we can do for limited English-speaking students is to limit their mathematical experience to strictly numerical work, thinking they will succeed better without words. Instead, these students need to be given many opportunities to share their mathematical thinking orally and in writing. For example, when a class activity involves small-group work, we can ensure that there are proficient English readers in every group so that all students can understand the task at hand. We can establish group norms for respect and participation that remind students that everyone in their group is responsible for making sure all other group members understand and can present their work. And we can be sure to call on all students to share the group's work with the class.

Likewise, the worst thing we can do for any student is to believe that because of some label or behavior, a student needs—or can only handle—less mathematics than other students. Too often, telling ourselves we're doing what's best for certain students, we lower the level of the mathematics we give them. We may focus primarily on computation or on one-step word problems strictly related to a rule they just learned. This narrow view of mathematics reinforces to these students that math is boring and irrelevant. Worse, our compassionate tendency to give students only what we think they can handle may just disguise our own low expectations, even to ourselves. Without intending to do so, we may sentence students to fulfill those low expectations and ensure that they will never be able to tackle a relevant, real problem they may eventually face later, simply because they will never have had any experience dealing with such problems.

Regardless of the ways students' talents or potential may be hidden, it's our responsibility as educators to look past the surface and realize they may have more talent than we think. If we understand the malleable nature of intelligence, confirmed by research, and if we act on what we know to offer students real opportunities to learn and grow smarter, perhaps we can move past the biases and low expectations we don't even realize we have.

Math Is *Supposed* to Make Sense!

Not long ago, I was called on to help my 14-year-old granddaughter, Maisey, who was struggling to pass algebra. Her motivation to *pass* algebra was strong—if she didn't, she wouldn't be eligible to play basketball. Her motivation to *learn* algebra in any meaningful way, however, was far less strong. She was convinced that there was nothing to be

·gained by trying to make sense of math, since there was little in math that made sense. Rather, she believed she just needed to find a way to remember which rule to use for which kind of problem. Maisey developed these beliefs over many years; getting past them is proving to be quite a challenge for her, as well as for the adults trying to help her.

Maisey's story is not unique. Unfortunately, many students, like many adults, have come to believe that math has more to do with abstract rules, memory tips, and magic tricks than it has to do with making sense. They have become used to being told what to do and have come to believe that mathematics may or may not make sense—often, the latter. The structure of our mathematics classrooms and the prevalence of a lecture approach to teaching can contribute to a student's belief that math just doesn't make sense. Changing that idea so that students come to not only believe, but demand, that math should make sense to them can be the difference between a program that simply covers material and one that turns students into mathematical thinkers.

What It Means to Make Sense of Mathematics

We should distinguish between *making sense* and the closely related ideas of *logic*, *reasoning*, and checking that an answer is *reasonable*. Making sense involves all of these things and more. When a student makes sense of what she's doing in mathematics, it's like a light bulb going on in her head. She sees how an answer or a process follows from what came before, she mentally verifies that what she sees is reasonable for the context or situation, she can see a reason why certain things were done, and what she sees fits with what she has previously learned, knows, or believes to be true. She feels comfortable that what she has done, or what she sees that someone else has done or said, *makes sense*. It becomes part of a bigger understanding that mathematics *makes sense* as a discipline—that the subject of mathematics has an underlying structure we can rely on. And the experience of making sense in that particular situation or for that particular problem contributes to a growing conviction that *math is supposed to make sense*.

Mathematical Habits of Mind

Arguably, the most important outcome for students in an effective mathematics program is the development of mathematical habits of mind—the ability to think mathematically, analyze situations, understand relationships, and adapt what they know to solve a wide range of problems, including problems that may not look like any they've encountered before. These habits of mind have been concisely characterized by Cuoco, Goldenberg, and Mark (2010) to include the following:

- **Performing thought experiments**—connecting experiences and previous understanding to mentally model a problem, situation, process, or operation.
- **Finding, articulating, and explaining patterns**— noticing regularity in situations, procedures, and so on and being able to accurately describe and explain the pattern.

- **Creating and using representations**—using different representations (words, pictures, objects, tables, graphs, symbols, equations, etc.) to solve problems and to develop and demonstrate understanding.
- **Generalizing from examples**—trying one or more specific examples as an entry point to a complex problem.
- **Articulating generality in precise language**—developing the nontrivial ability to clearly describe a mathematical pattern or relationship using correct mathematical vocabulary.
- **Expecting mathematics to make sense**—coming to believe, and even insist, that what we do in mathematics should make sense.

The last item on this list—expecting math to make sense—is without question the most important goal we should have for every student we see or for every student of every teacher we work with.

When Students Don't Make Sense of What They Do

I often tell the story of Marisa, a 5th grader highlighted in a video that is part of the Math Reasoning Inventory project (Burns, 2012). In a one-on-one situation, a teacher gives Marisa the following problem:

There are 295 students in the school. School buses hold 25 students. How many school buses are needed to fit all the students?

Marisa almost immediately dives into a calculation, lining up the number 25 under the number 295, writing an addition sign, and carefully (and accurately) adding 295 plus 25. She tells the teacher that her answer is 320 school buses. When the teacher asks her how she did it, she explains, "Since I heard the word 'all,' I figured it was plussing, so I plussed 295 and 25 and I got 320." When she first announces her answer before the explanation, she hesitates just an instant, perhaps considering that there probably would not need to be more buses than the number of students they are going to carry. But apparently Marisa decided that, since she had done what she had learned to do (paying attention to which clue words or key words might appear in a problem, and accurately computing), it didn't matter whether the answer made sense or not. After all, *this was math*.

Expecting Math to Make Sense

We often see included on problem solving lists or stated in learning standards that students should confirm that their answer is reasonable. Yet all of us have seen instances where a student will give an answer that obviously doesn't make any sense, as Marisa did. Unfortunately, too many students see "checking for reasonableness" as simply one more requirement to mindlessly check off, rather than thinking about whether their answer truly makes any sense or is reasonable for the problem, for a real situation, or in any other way. With an emphasis on rules, procedures, and tricks, we seem to have created a society in which many people (not just students) don't actually *expect* that math will make sense, so they aren't particularly concerned if it doesn't.

What an unfortunate situation—one of the most note-worthy characteristics of mathematics is that, by its very nature, it makes more sense than probably any other school subject. Mathematics has many dimensions and can be used in different ways, but its inherent structure, order, and logic unify mathematical topics and applications, and mathematics generally operates consistently and predictably. I'm afraid that the way we teach math sometimes belies that quality. In our zeal to cover a certain amount of material in a limited time, we can inadvertently short-circuit any effort toward understanding. We may convince ourselves that if students will just memorize the procedure, they'll do OK on the test. And sometimes, it just may not be practical to try to help every student conceptually understand the steps in a complex procedure like the long-division algorithm or the quadratic formula. But we can still help students come to see the inherent consistency within mathematics and to understand numbers, operations, and relationships well enough that what they see and do in mathematics makes sense to them.

We want students to believe deeply that mathematics makes sense—in generating answers to problems, discussing their thinking and other students' thinking, and learning new material. If something *doesn't* make sense, alarms should go off in their heads. It should be disturbing—or at least cause a minor upset. That moment of cognitive dissonance should lead the student to take some kind of action until whatever it is *does* make sense.

- If a student is solving a problem and an answer doesn't make sense (like Marisa's response that 320 buses would be needed to hold 295 students), that upset should cause the student to go back and reconsider the approach or calculation that led to that answer.
- If another student is explaining his thinking, and it doesn't make sense, the upset should lead the listener to ask a clarifying question.
- If the teacher is explaining a new mathematical concept, or the student otherwise encounters a new mathematical idea, and that concept or idea doesn't make sense, the upset should lead the student to ask a question or dig deeper until it does.

Consider what it would mean if every student—and every teacher—absolutely and positively believed that math is *supposed* to make sense. And whenever something mathematical didn't make sense to a student, that student would say, "Wait a minute. Wait a minute. That doesn't make sense to me (yet). And math is *supposed* to make sense!" If we were to accomplish that core goal, perhaps all of our other efforts to improve mathematics teaching and learning would have a real chance of success.

What Mathematics Do Students Need?

Most states' math standards today, including the Common Core State Standards for Mathematics, are based on a balance of concepts, computation, and problem solving. These three basic components of mathematics have been advocated for years. Unfortunately, some mathematics programs in the past heavily emphasized computation, sometimes undercutting the development of mathematical thinking and at the expense of students' conceptual understanding or their ability to apply what they learned to solve problems.

Mathematical Building Blocks: Concepts, Computation, Problem Solving

In order for students to learn mathematics in ways that can be useful, they need to make sense of the mathematics they're learning (concepts), know some skills and computational procedures (computation), and use what they've learned to solve a variety of problems (problem solving). When a program emphasizes too heavily or gives too little attention to one element, students are likely to achieve shallow, fleeting learning, at best.

The most common mistake in many school mathematics programs is focusing too strongly on computation, potentially sacrificing understanding and the ability to apply what is learned. Computation is indeed important, but for students to effectively learn facts and procedures, they need a solid conceptual foundation of *number sense* and *operation sense*. Number sense refers to a wide range of concepts related to numbers, such as visualizing what numbers represent, being able to take them apart and reassemble them, identifying a number that enumerates a set of objects, and grasping the concepts of place value beyond a superficial designation of which place a digit is in. Operation sense develops when students understand what it means to add, subtract, multiply, or divide, and can carry mental pictures that represent an operation, like being able to picture "8 × 3" as eight rows of three chairs or eight bowls of three marbles. When a student understands what numbers and operations are, it becomes easier to learn facts and procedures, and the learning is more likely to last.

Arguably, the most important mathematical content students need is the ability to use the concepts and skills they learn to solve problems. They need to be able to apply basic rules and procedures to solve straightforward word problems, such as finding how many pieces of pizza each person will get when sharing with two friends. But more than that, they need to have a strong enough foundation and confidence to tackle problems that may not look like routine problems they have seen before—problems that may require them to think about relationships, connect mathematical ideas, and extend what they already know. For example, they should be able to build on their knowledge of basic operations to solve a problem like determining what combinations of vehicles (cars, vans, and buses) might accommodate a group of students going on a field trip.

Fluency, Speed, and Calculators

There are different perspectives about whether conceptual understanding should precede the development of skills. Some mathematicians argue that understanding is essential, but that it can come after a skill or procedure has been memorized. However, strong evidence suggests that for developing computational fluency in K–12, conceptual understanding is a key component of lasting fact or skill learning, ideally preceding and accompanying that learning (National Council of Teachers of Mathematics, 2014b). Students who have developed an understanding of what an operation means and a strong sense of the numbers involved are far more likely to remember a fact like 4 × 7 than if they lack that kind of understanding. Experiences such as dealing with concrete objects or making pictures of four groups of seven (or arrangements of four rows of seven, etc.) can help students generate a mental picture so that the fact makes sense.

Focusing on speed as a requirement for fluency can lead to at least as many negative results as positive ones. I once visited a 7th grade classroom at the beginning of the school year (Seeley, 2015). The teacher noted that students seemed to have forgotten their multiplication facts (not unusual at that age, after a summer away from school), so she was giving a timed test each day to identify who needed remediation on various facts. I sat next to a young man who became so anxious over the timed test that he broke his pencil as he tried to fill in answers, most of which were incorrect. Yet, after the three minutes finally passed and the teacher had collected and was grading the papers, that same young man quickly and successfully completed a puzzle worksheet on exactly the same facts that had been on the timed test. A few minutes later, the teacher read his name as part of a list of students who needed remediation. Fluency should mean that students can access the facts they need when they need them without having to resort to time-consuming strategies, not that they can pass a timed test.

Calculators and other computational devices pervade all aspects of society and have become everyday aids accessible to essentially anyone. Such instruments can be powerful tools to enhance, but not replace, mathematics teaching and learning. There are times when calculators should not be used, especially when developing mental math skills or key computational procedures. But if we use them well, calculators can help students deal with cumbersome arithmetic and allow them to access complex problems they wouldn't be able to deal with otherwise. And a calculator can offer students the potential of representing mathematical relationships as graphs, tables, equations, and so on, making it a powerful learning and problem-solving resource. An effective teacher can help students learn to decide when to use a calculator and when it's just silly to use one (such as for multiplying by 10 or performing single-digit addition). Without explicitly dealing with this important decision-making skill in the classroom, we leave students on their own to figure out when to use technology, often choosing to use technology in situations in which it may not be helpful or appropriate.

Can Struggling Be Good for Students?

Teachers worry a lot about students who struggle. We hate to see frustration, insecurity, and impatience on a student's face. But as we now know, constructively struggling with challenging problems can help a student learn mathematics, as long as we provide the structure and support that will allow that struggle to progress toward understanding, meaning, thinking, and learning; in other words, to engage in *productive struggle*.

The positive benefits of productive struggle as part of learning have been discussed for some time (Hiebert & Grouws, 2007). But our increasing understanding of intelligence and the power of a growth mindset has brought productive struggle to the forefront of conversations about what needs to happen in math classrooms. Creating opportunities for productive struggle is one of the eight effective teaching practices identified by the National Council of Teachers of Mathematics (2014a).

How We Withhold Struggling

Unfortunately, many classrooms are structured in such a way that students rarely, if ever, have the opportunity to productively struggle with a mathematical concept or challenging math problem. We sometimes unintentionally withhold the opportunity to struggle from students across grades at all levels, from those we may view as less able to those we've accelerated into advanced material. We often withhold struggling with the best intentions, without ever realizing we're doing it, in many ways and for many reasons.

We sometimes slow down instruction out of compassion when we fear students might become frustrated, believing that we need to go over every rule or procedure in detail before expecting a student to use the procedure. By the time the student finally sees a problem, there's no thinking or struggling required, only a guessing game to remember which rule to use.

We might also avoid opportunities for struggle as we rush through material to cover content or finish our objectives for the year, especially if there's a test at the end. We may feel we simply don't have enough time to offer students the kinds of challenging tasks they might be able to sink their teeth into and struggle with as they work toward a solution. Or we might move our most advanced students through more content more quickly, denying even these allegedly bright students the opportunity to spend some time figuring out how to approach a problem they haven't been specifically taught.

In an effort to protect students from failure, we may try to tell them everything they need to know about how to solve a particular problem before they have to solve it. By habit or training, many of us are used to presenting a concept or rule in a well thought-out, step-by-step way. If we have a group of students we believe to be slower learners, it's a natural tendency to lower expectations for those students and assume they could become frustrated if they encounter a difficult problem. However, when we show students exactly how to solve a certain type of problem, we deny them the opportunity to think in advance how they might approach it. Thus, we may end up keeping them from struggling—but we also prevent them from learning how to persevere through a difficult problem or concept.

Even the way we ask and answer questions can interfere with students' opportunities to productively struggle. If we try to answer directly every question students ask, we may deny them a chance to think more deeply about what they're asking. And when we ask students too many scaffolding questions in a situation where they may be having difficulty with a task or concept, we sometimes end their struggle prematurely. I've heard myself short-circuit productive struggle while working with both students and teachers on more than one occasion. Just as someone is on the verge of really starting to think, I ask, "Had you thought about trying . . . ?" The wheels of thought come to a screeching halt, and a sigh of relief marks the end of the effort to make sense of what they're working on.

One of the most significant ways we keep students from engaging in productive struggle is by focusing on right answers and not capitalizing on their mistakes. Phil Daro (2012) has observed that teachers in the United States tend to prioritize helping students get the answer to a problem (hoping they will then be able to get the answer to similar problems). Teachers in Japan, on the other hand, tend to use problems as a vehicle for learning the intended mathematics, rather than seeing the solution to a problem as the end result. These teachers still value answers, but they mine a problem far more deeply than we tend to in this country, with an emphasis on students discussing their processes and thoughts about possible strategies and solutions, learning important mathematical ideas and procedures on the way to getting the answer.

Embrace Mistakes

A central aspect of organizing a classroom to foster productive struggle is generating rich discussion around students' processes and interim answers. And a key element of such discussions may involve looking at mistakes students have made as they've engaged in a task.

We've learned from the research on developing a growth mindset that dealing with mistakes is a powerful part of mathematics learning. In fact, Boaler (2015) and others suggest that it's through mistakes, not through generating right answers, that the most powerful learning happens, even though arriving at a correct answer remains our ultimate goal. (Carol Dweck reminds us that "Every time a student makes a mistake in math, they grow a synapse" [Boaler, 2015, p. 11].) In some cultures, students come to readily share and discuss their mistakes on the way to learning as an important step in the learning process.

When a teacher creates a classroom culture where mistakes are embraced, the classroom becomes a place where students feel safe to take a risk. As students learn that mistakes are not something to fear, they may become more willing to offer their thinking without worrying about whether they're going to feel embarrassed by sharing something incorrect. Being willing to make a mistake also contributes to students' willingness to productively struggle through what may at first seem difficult to them. The sign below, posted at the You-Cubed Summer Math Camp in 2015 (www.youcubed.org), could be a model for all mathematics classrooms.

> In this class, mistakes are
>
> EXPECTED
> INSPECTED
> RESPECTED

The Wrong Kind of Struggle

Some struggles may not be productive. Struggling isn't helpful if it doesn't lead to making sense of mathematics, learning a new mathematical idea, or exploring a possible solution to a problem. And it isn't helpful if students become so bogged down on one concept or process that frustration keeps them from seeing the bigger idea or prevents them from being able to tackle a problem. How can we recognize unproductive struggle and help students who may be stuck there?

The best way to help students who are struggling unproductively is by talking with—or more important, listening to—them in order to identify underlying misconceptions or confusions. Informal conversation or more structured formative assessment strategies can provide helpful information if we ask the right questions ("How did you decide to use a '1' when you wrote your equation?" or "Can you say more about what you tried right here?") and pay close attention to students' answers. Some students may need only a small clarification of a misunderstanding to be able to tackle a rich task. Others may be able to get past a computational barrier by using a calculator so that they can dig into a challenging problem without getting stalled trying to remember a particular rule or algorithm. Still others may need to reestablish a conceptual understanding by going through a well-chosen instructional task on previously covered topics. And some students may just be one thoughtful question away from turning unhelpful struggle into productive thinking. It's a mistake to think that we can use the same tool, strategy, or program to help every student stuck in unproductive struggle.

Opportunities for the Right Kind of Struggle

If we want students to learn how to think mathematically and make sense of what they're learning, we need to purposefully structure our classrooms so that students have the opportunity to tackle challenging problems and ideas, struggle a bit as they wrestle with possible approaches or solutions, and discuss their thinking with their peers in mathematical conversations.

Jim Stigler (Kivel, 2014) suggested that if students are to become flexible thinkers who can deal with problems they haven't specifically learned how to solve, they need recurring and sustained experience with three particular kinds of instructional opportunities:

- **Productive struggle**—to strengthen their thinking skills and deepen their mathematical understanding.
- **Deliberate practice**—to gain confidence by regularly tackling problems they may not already know how to solve and that call for them to struggle.
- **Explicit connections**—to see how new ideas, concepts, and skills connect to what they already know.

Connecting the results of a student's struggle to the student's previous learning and experience provides the payoff that makes the struggle worthwhile. In short, if we think of struggling as an instructional priority, rather than an indicator of a lack of smarts, we can help all students become proficient mathematical thinkers.

What If We Turn Teaching Upside Down?

If we want students to learn mathematical concepts and skills, make sense of mathematics, and become mathematical thinkers and problem solvers, we need to create classrooms that focus on thinking and sense making. Teachers who created such classrooms discovered the power of structuring their teaching around discourse within the context of students' engagement with rich, worthwhile tasks. While it is still important to target the *what* of mathematics teaching—the concepts, computation, and problem-solving skills we identify through standards and goals—helping students make sense of what they're learning and helping them develop as flexible problem solvers also calls for a shift in terms of *how* we teach.

An Environment for Making Sense

In order for students to learn how to think mathematically, they need to get used to daily routines that focus on discussions about their thinking. Students should come to expect that engaging in conversation about mathematics—mathematical discourse—is the typical way their math class operates. Too many students expect that, in math, they will be expected to sit quietly and listen to the teacher, trying to answer questions if called on. Some students are successful in this kind of environment and some are not, but few look forward to it.

Instead, we want to create a different expectation for students—that they will be part of a discussion in math class, that they will have a chance to mess around with interesting problems, talk about them, and even respectfully argue with each other. Students should develop the habit of justifying their point of view and asking clarifying questions of each other, all in the quest for everyone to make sense of the mathematics they're doing and learning. They should come to demand—of themselves, their classmates, and their teacher—that math is going to make sense. Classroom norms should be explicitly developed to focus on respect, collaboration, listening, questioning, understanding, and embracing mistakes. If such norms are developed and maintained across grades or even throughout a school or district as part of the "math culture," teachers can bypass having to establish these norms each year and become even more efficient and effective with their limited instructional time. Those students who were in the school the previous year will arrive in the fall already used to how the class will operate, ready to tackle new mathematical ideas and new problems.

Mistakes as a Stimulus for Discussion

For some time, teachers have recognized that when a student processes a mistake, and eventually arrives at a correct answer, something positive has happened. Combined with what we now know about the contribution of mistakes to growing intelligence, it seems clear that a classroom environment where mistakes are welcomed could create many opportunities for learning mathematics. Lightening our grip on getting correct answers quickly may allow us to view the structure of teaching differently.

Focus on Learning

As noted in our discussion of struggling, we can help students learn mathematics better if we shift our goal from helping students get answers to problems to using problems as a way to help students learn the mathematical content we want them to learn. Using problems in this way shifts the focus from getting answers as quickly as possible to digging into the mathematical ideas and concepts that emerge when students work through problems. When we view problems as a vehicle, rather than a destination, we can begin to envision a classroom organized differently from the traditional teacher-centered, lecture-based model. For example, consider the opportunities for student engagement and extended mathematical conversation in a lesson organized around the following problem for young children to explore combinations that add up to 10:

> There are 10 cars in the parking lot. Some of the cars are red, and some of the cars are black. How many red cars and how many black cars could be in the parking lot? Think of as many different combinations of cars as you can. Show your solutions in as many ways as you can with cubes, drawings, or words, and write an equation for each

solution. (Cited in National Council of Teachers of Mathematics, 2014a, as adapted from NC Department of Public Instruction, 2013)

With a rich, relevant problem like this, the focus is not on arriving at a particular answer, but rather on building number sense by having students dig into decomposing and recomposing a set of 10 objects in different ways.

Start with a Problem

If we create a safe and fertile classroom environment, and if we imagine that problems can be a powerful tool for learning mathematics, we can reconsider teaching models that may have outlived their usefulness. In particular, consider whether it ever makes sense today to structure a lesson in what we might consider a traditional approach: presenting a rule or procedure via teacher lecture, asking students to practice the procedure with teacher assistance until they can do it on their own, and then giving students one or more word problems in which they are expected to apply the procedure they just learned.

I suggest turning that model upside down: Start by giving students an engaging problem (either contextual or purely mathematical), and have them explore it, either alone or, preferably, with a partner or within a small group. Ideally, students will spend some time thinking about how they might approach the problem, consider what type of solution is called for or the approximate size the solution might be, and generally engage their minds as they productively struggle with the problem and the underlying relationships it might describe. When research mathematicians do the work of mathematics, they often describe exactly this kind of "messing around" as a first step. As they search for patterns, possible strategies, and eventual solutions, they may find themselves on paths that don't produce what they hoped they might. They learn from what didn't work as well as what did. Realizing that such exploration is part of the "real mathematics" done outside of school may help us move past an outdated belief that mathematics primarily involves learning clearly explained procedures and applying them accurately to certain types of problems.

When students have some time to explore and even struggle with a problem, our role as teacher becomes one of facilitating and stimulating conversation among students to ensure that they uncover and discuss the important mathematical ideas that lie within the problem. We want to structure ways for students to talk about different approaches they might have tried or solutions they've found. Within such a discussion, we try to ensure that students justify their thinking by responding to our probing questions and eventually learn to ask their own clarifying questions of each other. Finally, at some point, we help students make sense of their discussions within the context of the mathematical goals of the lesson. To close the lesson or at the end of a unit, our responsibility is to make sure that students know what mathematics they have learned.

The Problems We Choose

If we turn our teaching upside down, choosing appropriate tasks becomes the central point for our planning. The National Council of Teachers of Mathematics notes the central importance of implementing tasks that promote reasoning and problem solving as one of their eight critical teaching practices for effective teaching (2014a). Whether a task is used as an introduction to a new topic or to deepen understanding of a recently learned concept or skill, we need to select it for the opportunities it affords for engagement, reasoning, and discussion. A good task or problem has multiple access points—different ways of approaching the problem—and potentially more than one path toward a solution to the problem or completion of the task. If we're introducing the multiplication of fractions, for example, rather than showing students directly how to do the computation, we might instead ask them to figure out how to find $\frac{1}{6}$ of $\frac{1}{4}$ of a shape using pattern blocks. To deepen understanding of fraction multiplication, we might ask students to create a real-world situation to represent $\frac{2}{3} \times \frac{3}{4}$. Or to introduce systems of equations, we might ask them to compare cell phone plans with a fixed base rate and additional charges for each call or text (examples from National Council of Teachers of Mathematics, 2014a).

Wherever possible, a problem should be either relevant to a situation familiar to students or mathematically engaging in ways that are likely to interest them once they get into it. Not every task needs to be directly relevant to a student's experience, but the goal should be to offer students a range of problems that communicate the idea that math is used outside of school, ideally offering every student the opportunity to personally connect to some problems from time to time. And some wonderful tasks may not involve a real-world situation at all—they may simply be mathematically interesting, offering opportunities for students to explore and discuss relationships, patterns, and possibilities.

Move to You-We-I

One way to characterize upside-down teaching is to consider shifting the classroom away from an *I-We-You* model of teaching to a *You-We-I* model (Daro, 2012). The I-We-You model refers to the following steps:

- **I** (the teacher) am going to present to you (students) the procedure or concept for this lesson.
- **We** (students with guidance from the teacher) are going to practice together until you can do it on your own.
- **You** (students) are going to do the procedure on your own and apply the procedure or concept to solve related word problems.

An I-We-You model characterizes a type of teaching sometimes called *gradual release of responsibility*. While gradual release of responsibility may be a research-based method of teaching some skills in certain content areas—notably, in reading (Fisher & Frey, 2013; Pearson & Gallagher, 1983)—this model has not been shown to be an effective way to allow students to productively struggle with important mathematical ideas or unfamiliar problems.

Turning an I-We-You model of teaching upside down, we can instead adopt a You-We-I model:

- **You** (students) are going to "mess around" with a problem.
- **We** (students and the teacher) are going to have a discussion about what you tried, what you found, what worked, what didn't, and why you think certain approaches might be productive or not.
- **I** (the teacher) am going to help you connect your work to mathematical ideas and procedures and make sure you learn the intended mathematical outcomes of the lesson.

Shifting the focus of the class from the teacher's presentation to students' discussion of their thinking can yield powerful results in terms of depth of learning, lasting learning, and student attitudes. Even if a teacher shifts to an upside-down, You-We-I model only some of the time, students will benefit by seeing mathematics as something they can be part of.

Discover New Stars

In this kind of student-centered, problem-focused classroom, new stars are likely to emerge. Some teachers report that when they've made this kind of shift, more students seem to be successful in mathematics, and they tend to develop more positive attitudes about mathematics and about themselves as math students. When a classroom is no longer organized around a teacher's presentation of material, but rather engages students in wrestling with challenging problems and discussing ideas, many more students may be open to what's going on in math class, even if they previously seemed uninterested or thought they weren't the "math type." And when their answers and ideas are recognized as valuable, old ideas about the rigid nature of mathematics and who's smart in math can begin to disappear. We discover new stars in our classrooms in unexpected corners—students who may have been hiding from teachers and from themselves the fact that they really are "math people."

Communicate with Parents

One of the greatest barriers in changing our perspective on teaching mathematics is the long-standing belief of caring, involved parents that a teacher's responsibility is to teach all the rules and procedures a student needs before assigning problems. Many students and their families have come to believe that the way to succeed is by seeing or hearing clear explanations and replicating carefully worked-out examples. However, telling and showing doesn't allow for productive struggle and may not lead to deep learning.

It's important to reach out to families and caregivers to let them know that you may be doing things somewhat differently than they're used to, but that you're implementing research-based practices that are designed to help students learn to think and be able to tackle more challenging problems than they would be able to solve with more traditional teaching techniques. For some parents, this may be a message they don't want to hear. But deferring to parents' or students' requests for more direct presentation would mean spoon-feeding students and taking away their opportunity to struggle and think. Keeping parents informed about goals, purposes, and the rationale behind potential changes using such tools as parent conferences, back-to-school nights, or class newsletters can help minimize their discomfort with the shifts you make. Some may even applaud your efforts to help their children reach higher goals and achieve deeper learning.

What About the Test?

Spending more time on in-depth problems may seem too time-consuming to some teachers. They may worry that they won't have time to cover all of the content that will be assessed on the state accountability test. However, covering content without attending to learning can have disastrous results, both in terms of breadth and depth of knowledge. Students who race through content may have difficulty on a test. And even if they remember quickly covered facts or skills for the test, that learning may be short-lived and may not serve them well over time. On the other hand, teachers can help students learn mathematics deeply and also do well on a test. We can start by prioritizing the most important content for the grade or course, working collaboratively with our peers to identify which parts of the curriculum call for the most depth. For example, fractions may be addressed in several grade levels, but the major work on developing an understanding of what fractions are can likely be prioritized at a specific grade level. Another grade level might focus on the development of addition and subtraction of fractions, and so on. For the highest priority topics, concepts, and skills for a grade level or course, we can spend more time on in-depth problems and extended student discourse so that students come to make sense of critical building blocks of mathematical understanding. In doing so, students learn in ways that last and they're ready to demonstrate that learning, however it might be assessed.

Most important, many of today's tests are evolving into more comprehensive measures of learning than we've seen during the entire history of accountability testing. Advances in assessment theory are moving large-scale testing away from the previously predominant single-answer, multiple-choice format, where one item measures one discrete piece of knowledge. Some of the tests being developed to support the Common Core State Standards for Mathematics, for example, as well as a few other emerging tests, include longer test items and extended performance tasks. They no longer fit predictable patterns with three or four items per standard; rather, a test item or task may address more than one standard and may focus on mathematical thinking as much as mathematical content knowledge. For example, in a grade 6 sample performance task, the Smarter Balanced Assessment Consortium (SBAC) asks students to redesign cardboard boxes for a cereal company so that they use less cardboard and hold at least as much cereal as existing boxes, and the variety of other samples indicates SBAC's strong emphasis on this kind of in-depth assessment task (Smarter Balanced

Assessment Consortium, 2013). The Partnership for Assessment of Readiness for College and Careers (PARCC) offers a series of prototype items and tasks that demonstrate the shift toward a more complex set of test questions than previous state assessments (The Charles A. Dana Center at the University of Texas at Austin & Agile Mind, 2012).

The best way to prepare students to succeed on such tests seems clear—we need to make sure they have experience persevering in solving a wide range of problems, including problems that may not fit traditional categories of word problems. Our students need to develop the *flexible expertise* that Jim Stigler called for (Kivel, 2014), in which they are equipped to tackle problems even if they don't know in advance everything they might need to use to solve the particular problem. In a student-centered, problem-focused, upside-down classroom, students learn to deal with exactly this kind of problem, thus preparing them for whatever they may encounter on a test.

Where Can I Find Support?

Changing the way we teach can seem to be a daunting task, even if we're just trying to shift our practice in one or two key ways. It can be a bit easier to undertake if we go through the process with at least one colleague. The potential for success is even greater if teachers in a whole grade level or course, or even a whole school, go through the process together. Such a decision may lie in the hands of school or district leaders. But with or without a schoolwide commitment, we can gain tremendous support by working with others informally or formally. Not only is collaborating with friends and colleagues more effective and potentially less stressful, but the benefits for students can be far greater if norms and expectations are consistent from grade to grade.

Work Within and Across Grades and Courses

Communicating with other mathematics teachers within your school can be helpful in several ways. Some state standards, including the K–8 Common Core State Standards for Mathematics, specify a small number of topics or skills for each grade level as primary focal areas for that grade. Whether your standards identify such focal points or not, explicitly agreeing with colleagues on major priorities for a grade or course will allow you to spend more time on topics with the highest payoff, even if other content receives less attention. One of the greatest concerns teachers express is a lack of time for students to learn content in deep, lasting, and meaningful ways. If we can agree on a few priorities, we can shift the focus of valuable instructional time to allow students time to finish at least the most critical topics and skills. As long as next year's teacher knows which topics were treated in-depth and which were lightly introduced or reviewed, students can focus on (and finish learning) important mathematics each year, ultimately building a powerful set of mathematical tools and thinking skills. This kind of planning and collaboration is especially effective when working with colleagues in adjacent grades.

Working across schools whenever possible can also yield significant benefits for students. As students move from elementary to middle or middle to high school, they deal with a myriad of developmental and social, as well as academic, changes. When teachers can provide some level of continuity in terms of how math classrooms operate and how student discourse is valued and rewarded, they increase the likelihood that students will be able to build on what they've previously learned to succeed with increasingly complex problems and content.

Rely on Your Professional Learning Community

Many schools and school systems have implemented the use of professional learning communities, sometimes with significant gains for both teachers and students. Unfortunately, sometimes this potentially powerful structure can be watered down to become little more than a series of glorified faculty meetings. In some schools, professional learning communities have been reduced to superficial recipes and checklists: how many meetings we held, who attended, what we did, and so on.

We can maximize the likelihood that a professional learning community will lead to greater teacher professionalism and increased student learning by asking ourselves important questions focused on the meanings of the words *professional, learning,* and *community* (Seeley, 2014):

- **Professional**—Are we centered on a professional commitment to help all students learn important mathematical content, processes, and thinking skills? Are we treating all members of the learning community as committed professionals, respecting their time and valuing their contributions?

- **Learning**—Is our focus of attention student learning, including the critical elements of making sense of mathematics and learning to think mathematically? Are we measuring student learning based on multiple measures and day-to-day formative assessment, and not just on overall scores on the large-scale accountability test? Are we using student work samples as indicators of learning and as a basis for our discussions?

- **Community**—Are we taking advantage of the power of our collaboration to learn from each other so that we all improve our teaching to help every student learn to think mathematically?

If we work together around a shared vision of what it means to know mathematics and think mathematically, and build on a shared commitment to help every student achieve those goals, we are much more likely to succeed.

Conclusion

Teaching mathematics does not need to look like it did when I was in school, or even like it did when I learned how to teach. In fact, teaching mathematics today *cannot* look like it used to. The world today demands that we prepare students to be knowledgeable, flexible thinkers who can approach problems from different perspectives and apply what they know in unexpected situations. Employers need workers coming from every level of education to be creative thinkers and collaborative problem solvers. Only by creating classrooms where students productively struggle with many different kinds of problems, discuss and justify their thinking, respect and value the contributions of others, and realize that success is more about thinking and working hard than it is about who's born with an innate ability to "do math," will we succeed at helping the next generation of students become mathematical thinkers and problem solvers.

To give your feedback on this publication and be entered into a drawing for a free ASCD Arias e-book, please visit **www.ascd.org/ariasfeedback**

ASCD | arias™

ENCORE

WHAT CAN WE DO?

The most important purpose of this book is to stimulate action. That action may include seeking out additional resources, making changes in your own classroom, or creating collaborative structures with colleagues. To help you identify next steps, consider completing the To-Do List exercise at the end of this section after reflecting on the following questions, either individually or in discussion with others.

Reflection/Discussion

- Who's Smart in Math?
  — How well do you support students in becoming smarter? What can you do differently to help more students become smarter?
  — In what ways are your students' talents and potential hidden below the surface to keep you (and them) from noticing that they may be smarter than we think?
  — How can you help students change their mindset about what it means to be smart in math?

- Math Is *Supposed* to Make Sense!
  — How many of your students expect that mathematics will make sense?
  — How can you help students learn to be bothered when something in math doesn't make sense to them? What can you do to help more students

internalize the expectation that math is supposed to make sense?

- What Mathematics Do Students Need?
  — Which components of a comprehensive, balanced mathematics program do you think you offer most effectively? How might you strengthen your attention to other components?
  — How can you connect an understanding of underlying concepts with the skills students learn?

- Can Struggling Be Good for Students?
  — How long do you let students struggle with a complex problem before offering assistance? What kinds of assistance do you tend to offer, and how well do you think your assistance supports productive struggle?
  — How can you help students develop the confidence and persistence to persevere through a difficult problem?

- What If We Turn Teaching Upside Down?
  — How often do you provide students with the opportunity to wrestle with a problem without first knowing all of the concepts and procedures that might be necessary or useful to solve the problem?
  — How can you communicate to students and their families the importance of not telling students

everything they might need to know before giving them good problems?

- Where Can I Find Support?
  - — How often do you communicate or work with your math-teaching colleagues for your grade or course? How often do you interact with math-teaching colleagues from grade levels below and above yours, either within your school or from other schools? How can you increase the number of opportunities for such collaboration?
  - — How do you use (or how can you use) a professional learning community to improve mathematics teaching and enhance student learning?

Your Personal To-Do List

In order to commit yourself to the action(s) you will take to strengthen your mathematics teaching or the teaching of those you support, I suggest making a to-do list. Identify one or two things you'd like to do, study, or try in the next week; one or two things you'd like to do, study, or implement in the next six months; and one or more things you'd like to put into action for the next school year. Determine what resources you'll need in order to accomplish your goals and who you might need to work with. Decide how you will realistically measure success.

Resources for Upside-Down Teaching

Chapin, S. H., O'Connor, C., & Anderson, N. C. (2013). *Classroom discussions in math: A teacher's guide for using talk moves to support the Common Core and more, grades K–6* (3rd ed.). Sausalito, CA: Math Solutions.

Featherstone, H., Crespo, S., Jilk, L. M., Oslund, J. A., Parks, A. N., & Wood, M. B. (2011). *Smarter together! Collaboration and equity in the elementary math classroom*. Reston, VA: National Council of Teachers of Mathematics.

Gojak, L. M. (2011). *What's your math problem? Getting to the heart of teaching problem solving*. Huntington Beach, CA: Shell Education.

Illustrative Mathematics. (n.d.). Webpage. Retrieved from http://www.illustrativemathematics.org

National Council of Teachers of Mathematics. (1991). Professional standards for teaching mathematics. Reston, VA: Author.

Parrish, S. (2014). *Number talks: Helping children build mental math and computation strategies, grades K–5.* Sausalito, CA: Math Solutions.

Smith, M. S., & Stein, M. K. (2011). *5 practices for orchestrating mathematics discussions*. Reston, VA: National Council of Teachers of Mathematics.

Additional resources and programs are listed in Message 12, "Upside-Down Teaching," in Seeley, C. L. (2014). *Smarter than we think: More messages about math, teaching, and learning in the 21st century*. Sausalito, CA: Math Solutions.

References

References

Boaler, J. (2015). *Mathematical mindsets: Unleashing students' potential through creative math, inspiring messages and innovative teaching*. San Francisco: Jossey-Bass.

Burns, M. (2012). Math reasoning inventory [Website]. Retrieved from https://mathreasoninginventory.com

The Charles A. Dana Center at the University of Texas at Austin. (2016). Academic Youth Development [Website]. Retrieved from http://utdanacenter.org/ayd

The Charles A. Dana Center at the University of Texas at Austin & Agile Mind. (2012). About the prototyping project [Webpage]. Retrieved from http://ccsstoolbox.agilemind.com/parcc/PARCCPrototype_main.html

Cuoco, A., Goldenberg, E. P., & Mark, J. (2010). Contemporary curriculum issues: Organizing a curriculum around mathematical habits of mind. *Mathematics Teacher, 103*(9), 682–688.

Daro, P. (2012, April). Untitled presentation to the Association of State Supervisors of Mathematics. Philadelphia, PA.

Dweck, C. S. (2006). *Mindset: The new psychology of success*. New York: Ballantine Books.

Fisher, D., & Frey, N. (2013). *Better learning through structured teaching: A framework for the gradual release of responsibility* (2nd ed.). Alexandria, VA: ASCD.

Hiebert, J., & Grouws, D. A. (2007). The effects of classroom mathematics on students' learning. In F. K. Lester Jr. (Ed.), *Second handbook of research on mathematics teaching and learning* (pp. 371–404). Reston, VA: National Council of Teachers of Mathematics.

Kivel, L. (2014, September 11). Creating opportunities for students to become flexible experts [Blog post]. Retrieved from Carnegie Commons Blog at http://www.carnegiefoundation.org/blog/creating-opportunities-students-become-flexible-experts/

National Council of Teachers of Mathematics. (2014a). Principles to actions: Ensuring mathematical success for all. Reston, VA: Author.

National Council of Teachers of Mathematics. (2014b). Procedural fluency in mathematics. Position statement. Reston, VA: Author.

NC Department of Public Instruction. (2013). First grade tasks [Wiki page]. Retrieved from http://commoncoretasks.ncdpi.wikispaces.net/First+Grade+Tasks

Pearson, P. D., & Gallagher, M. (1983). The instruction of reading comprehension. *Contemporary Educational Psychology, 8*(3), 317–344.

Seeley, C. L. (2014). *Smarter than we think: More messages about math, teaching, and learning in the 21st century.* Sausalito, CA: Math Solutions.

Seeley, C. L. (2015). *Faster isn't smarter: Messages about math, teaching, and learning in the 21st century* (2nd ed.). Sausalito, CA: Math Solutions.

Seeley, C. L. (2016). *Building a math-positive culture: How to support great math teaching in your school.* Alexandria, VA: ASCD.

Smarter Balanced Assessment Consortium. (2013). *Smarter Balanced Assessment Consortium: Practice test scoring guide, grade 6 performance task.* Retrieved from http://www.smarterbalanced.org/wordpress/wp-content/uploads/2015/08/Grade6MathPT.pdf

Related ASCD Resources

At the time of publication, the following ASCD resources were available (ASCD stock numbers appear in parentheses). For up-to-date information about ASCD resources, go to www.ascd.org. You can search the complete archives of *Educational Leadership* at http://www.ascd.org/el.

ASCD EDge®
Exchange ideas and connect with other educators interested in math on the social networking site ASCD EDge at http://ascdedge.ascd.org.

Print Products
Building a Math-Positive Culture: How to Support Great Math Teaching in Your School (ASCD Arias) by Cathy L. Seeley (#SF116068)
Engaging Minds in Science and Math Classrooms: The Surprising Power of Joy by Eric Brunsell & Michelle A. Fleming (#113023)
Engineering Essentials for STEM Instruction: How do I infuse real-world problem solving into science, technology, and math? (ASCD Arias) by Pamela Truesdell (#SF114048)
Learning to Love Math: Teaching Strategies That Change Student Attitudes and Get Results by Judy Willis (#108073)
STEM Leadership: How do I create a STEM culture in my school? (ASCD Arias) by Traci Buckner & Brian Boyd (#SF114081)
Succeeding with Inquiry in Science and Math Classrooms by Jeff C. Marshall (#113008)

For more information: send e-mail to member@ascd.org; call 1-800-933-2723 or 703-578-9600, press 2; send a fax to 703-575-5400; or write to Information Services, ASCD, 1703 N. Beauregard St., Alexandria, VA 22311-1714 USA.

About the Author

Cathy Seeley is committed to high-quality mathematics for every student. She has worked as a teacher, district mathematics coordinator, and Texas state mathematics director for grades K–12 and is a sought-after speaker, having spoken in all 50 states and around the world. After returning in late 2001 from teaching mathematics (in French) as a Peace Corps volunteer in Burkina Faso, Cathy was elected to serve as President of the National Council of Teachers of Mathematics. In that role, she received an EXCEL Gold Award for her President's Message "Embracing Accountability." She has appeared on television and radio and authored or coauthored various publications including textbooks. Her book *Faster Isn't Smarter: Messages About Math, Teaching, and Learning in the 21st Century* received a 2010 AEP Distinguished Achievement Award. It was followed in 2014 by the publication of *Smarter Than We Think: More Messages About Math, Teaching, and Learning in the 21st Century.* Cathy recently retired as a Senior Fellow with the Charles A. Dana Center at the University of Texas, where she worked on state and national policy and improvement efforts, with a focus on prekindergarten –grade 12 mathematics. Visit Cathy's website at www.cathyseeley.com.

WHOLE CHILD
TENETS

ASCD's Whole Child approach is an effort to transition from a focus on narrowly defined academic achievement to one that promotes the long-term development and success of all children. Through this approach, ASCD supports educators, families, community members, and policymakers as they move from a vision about educating the whole child to sustainable, collaborative actions.

Making Sense of Math: How to Help Every Student Become a Mathematical Thinker and Problem Solver relates to the **engaged, supported,** and **challenged** tenets.

1 HEALTHY
Each student enters school healthy and learns about and practices a healthy lifestyle.

2 SAFE
Each student learns in an environment that is physically and emotionally safe for students and adults.

3 ENGAGED
Each student is actively engaged in learning and is connected to the school and broader community.

4 SUPPORTED
Each student has access to personalized learning and is supported by qualified, caring adults.

5 CHALLENGED
Each student is challenged academically and prepared for success in college or further study and for employment and participation in a global environment.

LEARN. TEACH. LEAD.

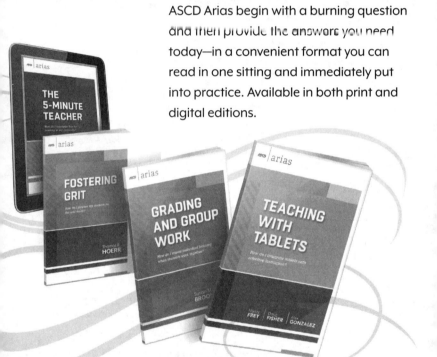